Mommy, Can I Ride on The Big White Bus?

ALYSSA ROMERO

This story, this real-life story, is for the ones that I live for every day. For the ones that have shown strength, growth, struggles, sadness, and joy. Who have experienced the ups and downs, different sceneries, and memorable adventures and who continue to explore and grow.

This is for you.

This is for my Jess, my Noah, my Isaac, and my Forever. I thank you for letting me be your mom. I thank you for letting me be your wife. I thank you for showing me that I have done something right in my life. I will continue to support and be your biggest fan, cheering you on in life.

Mommy loves you!

There are many kinds of busses.

You have small busses,

big yellow school busses,

double-decker busses,

and city busses.

But there is a bus that is very extra
special to some, and it is a big white bus.

This big white bus takes mommies and daddies, brothers and sisters, aunts and uncles, and many special people to places that some cannot go to.

Every now and then, Daddy has to leave for work with his friends and brothers, and when they do, they get on this special big white bus. And sometimes this bus takes a long time to come back.

Little Noah would see the big white bus in many different places.

He would see them close to home and sometimes driving on the road.

And every time he would see this special white bus, he would ask,

"Mommy, can I ride on the big white bus?"

With all his bags packed and loaded, it is time for Daddy to leave for work.

With much excitement, Noah sees the big white bus. Daddy gives big hugs of . love and tight squeezes and says, "I will see you later. Daddy has to go to work now and I will be home soon."

As Noah watches the big white bus drive down the road, squeezing his mommy's hand tightly, we wave goodbye and watch the big white bus drive away.

"Mommy, can I ride on the big white bus?" asks Noah.

"Not today. Only Daddy can ride on the big white bus. Maybe one day." Mommy replies.

Many years go by and from time to time we would say "see you later, Daddy" and to the big white bus.

And there were many times we would say "welcome home" to the big white bus. And each time it would bring lots of tears and joy.

Noah is much older now, and one day after he has come back from school, he says to his mommy, "Do you remember every time I asked to ride the big white bus?"

Mommy looks at Noah with a little tear in her eye. She answers, "Yes, I remember."

"Mommy, it's time for me to ride on the big white bus."

As Mommy looks at Noah, she knows it is his turn.

It is Noah's turn to ride on the special big white bus, just like Daddy used to.

As Noah gets on the bus, he asks, "Mommy, can I ride on the big white bus?"

Mommy answers, "Yes, my son, you can now ride on the big white bus."

Noah is happy that he finally gets to ride on that special big white bus that he always used to wave goodbye to.

Noah gives his big hugs and tight squeezes and says, "I will see you later."

Mommy, Daddy, Sister, and Brother wave to the big white bus that Noah is now riding on.

CPSIA information can be obtained
at www.ICGtesting.com
Printed in the USA
LVHW071014280421
685588LV00019B/75

* 9 7 8 1 6 4 9 9 0 5 5 0 5 *